BEANO

£2·25

Printed and Published in Great Britain by D. C. THOMSON & CO., LTD., 185 Fleet Street, London EC4 2H

ISBN 0 85116 297 5

EDITOR
HOPE YOU ENJOY THIS BOOK—JUST THE THING FOR A GOOD LONG LAUGH!

The Beano BOOK 1985
START
FINISH
HA-HA-HA-HA-HA-HA-HA-HA-HA-HA-HA-HA-HA-HA-HA-HA-HA-HA-HA-HA-HA-HA-HA-HA-HA-HA

Who's asking questions—any suggestions?

I'M NOT ANSWERING A LOT OF SILLY QUESTIONS.

So—
WALTER'S HOUSE
I'VE MADE MY OWN QUESTIONNAIRE.

I'M DOING A SURVEY. COULD YOU TELL ME HOW MANY SOAP FLAKES YOU HAVE?
OO! I'D LOVE TO!

ONE, TWO . . .
SOAP FLAKES
SOAP SOAP SOAP
SOAP FLAKES

Much later—
. . . 7,892, 7,893 . . .
SOAP FLAKES
SOAP FLAKES
SOAP FLAKES

Bubble trouble!

GET THEM, DOCTOR!
BAH!

And soon—
EXCUSE ME, WHAT DO YOU THINK OF THE RUMOUR THAT RED JELLY BABIES MAKE YOUR HAIR TURN GREEN?
JELLY BABIES
EH? IS THAT RIGHT?

FLIP
FLIP
OUT WITH YOU, NASTY RED JELLY BABIES!

CHOMP! GREAT PIECE OF MENACING!

NO-ONE WILL ANSWER MY QUESTIONS. WILL YOU DO IT?
OH, GO ON THEN!

WHAT IS THE FUNNIEST THING YOU'VE SEEN TODAY?
EHM . . .

Dear oh dear—Dad can hear!

Whacking good fun for you!

SPOT THE SLIPPER

DENNIS HAS HIDDEN DAD'S SUPPLY OF 20 WHACKING SLIPPERS—CAN YOU FIND THEM ?

Billy Whizz

WON'T YOU EVER STOP RUSHING ABOUT, BILLY?

ERK!
CRASH!
BUT, DAD, IF I STOP RUNNING AROUND I MIGHT GET FAT . . .
OOF!
. . . THINK OF THE DAMAGE I'D CAUSE!
CRUNK!

What if Billy was stiff!

GOSH! THAT'S RIGHT! JUST STAY AS FAST AS YOU ARE AND GO AND GET THIS WEEK'S ISSUE AT TOP WHIZZ SPEED!
TOSS
So—
CAN'T DO WITHOUT " THE BEANO " —I ALWAYS GET FIRST READ, YOU KNOW!
WHISPER! ACTUALLY, READERS, HE DOESN'T—I READ IT AT WHIZZ SPEED ON MY WAY BACK!

GNASHER SNAPS

GNERK! ME AND MY PAL CHASED A CAT UP ON THIS ROOF—ANY IDEAS HOW WE CAN GET DOWN AGAIN?

The
BASH STREET
Kids
WHIRRR!
SMIFFY-THICK-HEAD
WE ENJOY A GAME OF CRICKET.
ERK!
LET GO OF THE BALL, YOU FOOL!
CRAACK!
HOWZAT?

Silly fool closes school!

NO SCHOOL! BOO-HOO-HOO!
SCHOOL
SOAP
CUTHBERT CRINGEWORTHY, SCHOOL SWOT

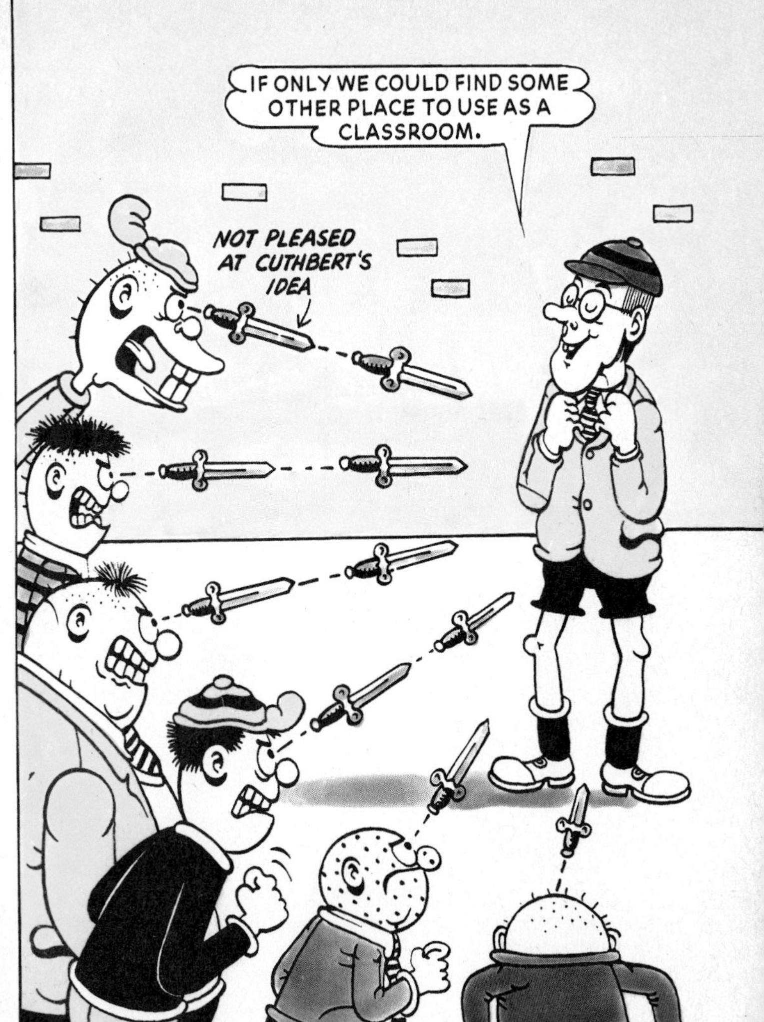
IF ONLY WE COULD FIND SOME OTHER PLACE TO USE AS A CLASSROOM.
NOT PLEASED AT CUTHBERT'S IDEA

I KNOW—WE CAN USE CRINGEWORTHY TOWERS!
EVEN LESS PLEASED
GNASHING OF TEETH!

So—
IN YOU COME; WIPE YOUR FEET.
CRINGEWORTHY TOWERS
THANKS, MATER!
MUTTER!

Brush off—from a toff!

The Kids fancy themselves as performers.
SIZE 7
TAP! TAP!
But—
BOO!
TERRIBLE!
GET OFF!
RUBBISH!
DON'T 'PHONE US . . .
DON'T THINK WE'RE WANTED IN THERE!
PONK!

FARMER INNES DEN'S ALLOWED US TO USE HIS BARN.

LET'S HAVE A BARN DANCE!
OINK!

TAKE YOUR PARTNER BY THE HAND, SWING HIM ROUND, YOU'RE LOOKING GRAND . . .
TWANG!
ENJOYING THEMSELVES

Hip-hooray—holiday!

CLICK!
CLICK!
BRAVO! YOU'VE PUSHED THE SCHOOL TOGETHER AGAIN!
IN YOU GO FOR LESSONS!
BASH ST. SCHOOL
ALL FATTY'S FAULT!
VERY, VERY ANGRY

FOOTBALL DAFT is BALL BOY

Who in Roger's town will be the dodging clown?

GOOD DODGE SO FAR!
PITY THE RIVER'S FROZEN! HAW-HAW!
YES, TOMMY COULD BE OUR TOWN'S WORST DODGER!
BILLY'S GOING TO SPY ON SWOTTY SIMPKINS' HOMEWORK.

A soaking—no joking!

THAT COULD HAVE BEEN A GREAT DODGE . . .
BOING!
ROVERS F.C
. . . EXCEPT ROVERS ARE PLAYING AWAY TODAY!
LET ME OUT!
ROVERS F.C. OFFICIAL TEAM COACH

HARD TO PICK THE WORST DODGER FROM THAT LOT.
FANCY A DRIVE, ROGER?
OLD IE

HOW BORING! I DON'T LIKE BEING SEEN IN DAD'S OLD BANGER.

I'LL JUST HIDE IN HERE!

Wonder blunder!

LORD SNOOTY

HMM!
NNNNNN

ALL THE OTHER KIDS HAVE PETS—THINK I'LL GET ONE.

Back at Bunkerton Castle—
CAN I HAVE A PET GOLDFISH, AUNT MAT?
I DON'T THINK THAT WOULD BE A GOOD IDEA!

OH, WHY?
BECAUSE OF MY PETS!
SLURP!
MMMMM!

Sad lad—soon glad!

YOU BET!
THANKS A LOT, SNOOTY!
YAHOO! I WOULDN'T HAVE BEEN ABLE TO GET A RIDE ON A GOLDFISH'S BACK! CHUCKLE!
TOO TRUE!
FISH FOOD
WOW! LOOK AT SNOOTY!
SPLOOSH!

Below you'll see a letter for B.B.!

TRIP
. . . BUT THE TREE FOULS HIM! TALK . . .
WILLIE HAS A SHOT. TALK, CHATTER . . .
WHUMP!
. . . BUT THE BALL HITS THE POST, AND THE POSTMAN ISN'T TOO PLEASED! CHATTER . . .
THUD!
GPO

Look at the note Ball Boy wrote!

FOOTBALL DAFT

What can it be Plum wants to see?

HEH! IT'S WORKING! HE'S TICKLISH!
TICKLE
CHUCKLE! HMM!
OFF I GO AGAIN!

SWAY
UM BRIDGE DOESN'T SEEM TOO SAFE!
FRAY
CREAK!

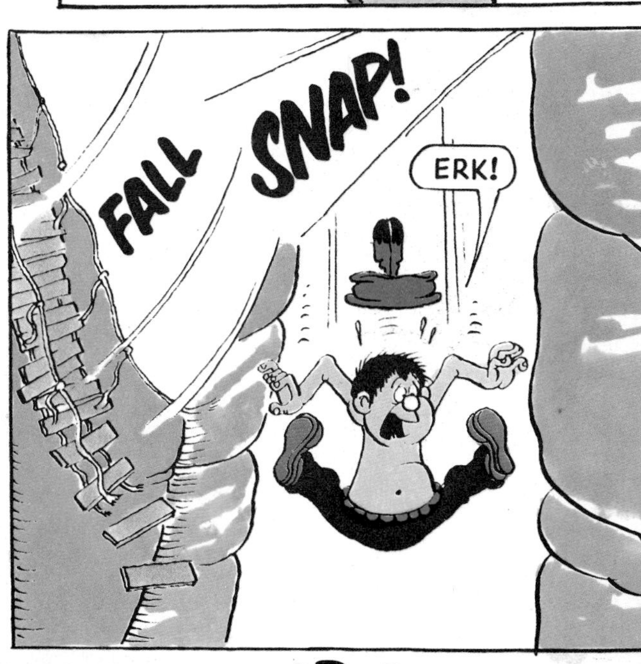
FALL
SNAP!
ERK!

PHEW! LUCKY THIS TREE WAS HERE!
SWING

FLIP-P
WHE-E!
MUST HURRY NOW!

You just can't beat um ringside seat!

ALL IN A DAY'S WORK
By DENNIS's MUM
8.00 A.M.
TRIED TO GET DENNIS UP FOR SCHOOL . . .
WAKEY-WAKEY!
. . . GOT GNASHER'S COLD NOSE TO HELP ME!
8.30 A.M.
GAVE DENNIS HIS PORRIDGE— WISH HE'D STOP READING AT THE TABLE.
GUZZLE! CHOMP!
BEANO
MUM'S PORRIDGE IS AWFUL!
11.00 A.M.
DECIDE TO HAVE JAM TARTS FOR ELEVENSES . . .
TUG
. . . WISHED I HADN'T TOLD DENNIS NOT TO EAT A SINGLE TART!

2.30 P.M.
TIME TO DO DENNIS'S WASHING . . .
. . . DISCOVER HE HAD SHERBET IN HIS TROUSER POCKET!
.00 P.M.
A VACUUM- CLEANER SALESMAN ARRIVES TO GIVE A DEMONSTRATION . . .
. . . GLAD HE MISTOOK GNASHER FOR A RUG!
4.00 P.M.
A PILE OF MUD COMES INTO THE HOUSE . . .
. . . FIND THAT DENNIS HAS BEEN PLAYING RUGBY!
SHAKE
.00 P.M.
DENNIS DOES HIS HOMEWORK— WHAT A SURPRISE!
I must not put worms down Walter's neck.
I must not put worms down Walter's neck
I must not put worms
9.00 P.M.
TIME FOR DENNIS TO GO TO BED . . .
. . . I WONDER WHAT HE DREAMS OF?
MISCHIEF

SCOOSH!
GRANDPA
I'LL GIVE YOU TWO POUNDS TO DELIVER THIS LETTER, GRANDPA.
THIS IS EASY MONEY —IT'S JUST ALONG THE ROAD.
Soon—
SEE? HERE IN NO TIME AT ALL!
27/4

But—
SPLOSH!

GLUB!

On the floor after tricks galore!

Oh, gosh! What a wash!

GNASHER SNAPS
NEEDING SOME HELP TO EAT THAT, TINY?

PUP PARADE
WITH THE BASH St. PUPS
Bet I could tell which one of you is barking, even blindfolded!
Never!

Right! Start!
No looking through your mouth, now!
SNIFFY DIMMEST OF DOGS

MUFFLED BARK!

Manfrid! You can hardly hear him through his collar!

This bright spark knows every bark!

BARK!
Hmm!
I can't quite place that bark!
Your stupid contest's given me a headache!
PROD
ERK! Brutus from along the street!
Serves Bones right! Boaster!
RAGE!
He who barks last barks longest, er...

Very good fun with food!

CHUCKLE! IT'S GOOD FOR MENACING, TOO!

DID YOU KNOW FISH IS A FINE BRAIN FOOD?
REALLY?
GOOD FOOD

WHY NOT TRY SOME?

NOW SAL'S GOT FISH ON THE BRAIN!
YOU HORRORS! NOW I'M SCARED TO MOVE!
GOOD FOOD

Eventually—
THANKS, MUM! NOW TO GET EVEN WITH THOSE TWO.
GOOD FOOD

So—
DID YOU KNOW VEGETABLE MARROWS ARE BAD FOR YOUR FEET?
HUH! WHAT NONSENSE!

But—
IT'S TRUE! WATCH!
LIFT!
ROLL
ROLL
CRUNCH!
CRUNCH!

HEH-HEH! I FIXED THOSE GOOD-FOR-NOTHINGS!
HOWL!

GNASHER'S TALE

I CAN'T RESIST CHASING A CAT!

QUICK—INTO THIS HOUSE!

Inside the house—
WE'LL HIDE UP THE CHIMNEY!

But—
GNASH! GNASH!

The chimney man is a Gnasher fan!

GNASHER
SNAPS

THE THINGS SOFTY DOGS'LL DO TO KEEP THEIR PAWS DRY!

Snakes alive—a cattle drive!

The 3 BEARS

BY THE LIGHT OF THE SILVERY . . .
. . . MOO N!
IDEA!
DO THE TRICK!
So—
WE'LL SNEAK UP CLOSE DISGUISED AS A COW!
A SIX-LEGGED COW? MIGHTY STRANGE!

Not a cow now!

HEY! THAT STEER HASN'T BEEN BRANDED YET!
I'LL DO IT NOW!
WAH! WE'RE OFF!
CHUCKLE! FOOLED THEM!

THIS ISN'T A BRANDING IRON— I WAS JUST COOKING MYSELF A HOT POTATO! HEH-HEH!

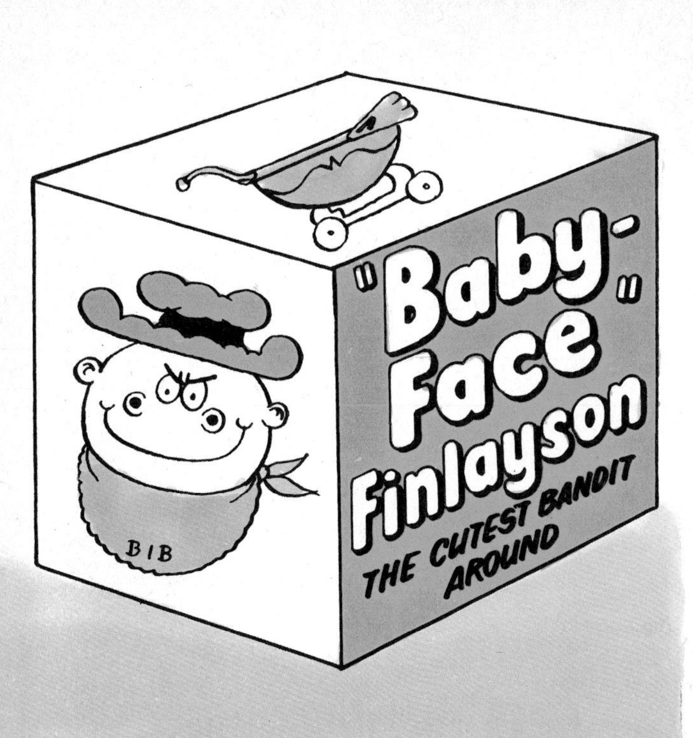
"Baby-Face" Finlayson
THE CUTEST BANDIT AROUND
BIB

One night—
TOY MUSEUM
A FINE PLACE TO BREAK INTO!

I'LL USE MY TOY TO HELP ME.
TOY MOLE
BIB

SPLENDID BURROWING CREATURE, THAT.
DIG
WHIRR!
BIB

Which toy for our bandit boy?

SUPER!
POP! POP!
AFRICAN POP GUN
WONDER WHAT THIS IS?
FROM TIBET
BIFF!
PYOING!
FROM TIBET
Next morning—
HAR-HAR! LOOKS LIKE "BABY-FACE" FOUND THE YAK-IN-THE-BOX!
SOMEWHAT DAZED
FROM TIBET

FOOTBALL DAFT
is BALL BOY
SCHOOL DINING ROOM
PASS THE SALT? SURE!
PASS

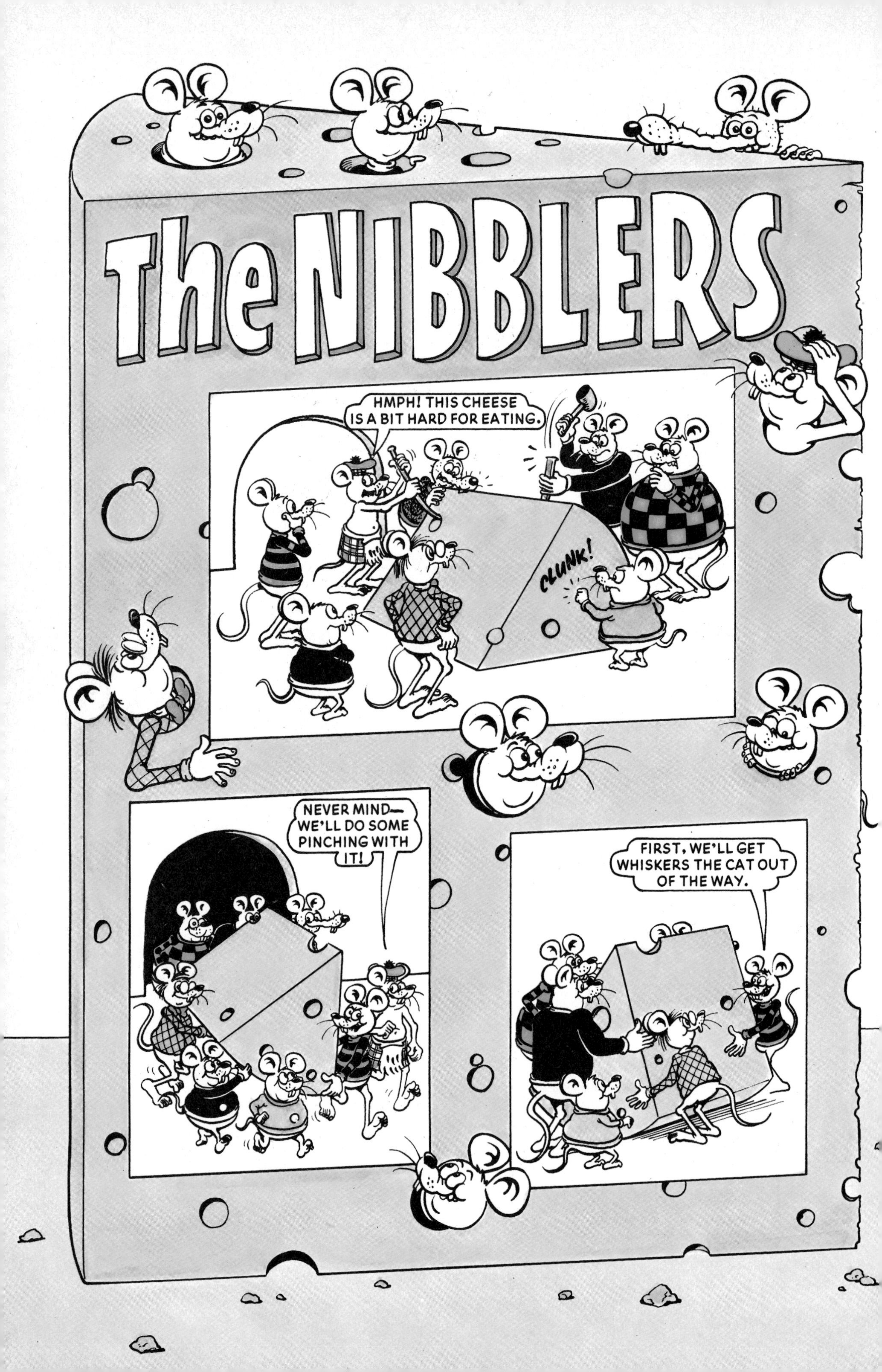
The NIBBLERS
HMPH! THIS CHEESE IS A BIT HARD FOR EATING.
CLUNK!
NEVER MIND— WE'LL DO SOME PINCHING WITH IT!
FIRST, WE'LL GET WHISKERS THE CAT OUT OF THE WAY.

What a sight—mice in flight!

Wahey! Super custard spray!

HERE IS A NEWSFLASH— WE WILL NOW HAVE SIXTEEN PAGES ALL ABOUT THE LATEST ADVENTURES OF LITTLE ME...

MINNIE the MINX NEWS
"BEANO" TV

A Minx of many parts

MY OWN MINI-BOOK, ALL TO MYSELF— HEH! HEH!

WHO NEEDS ALL THE OTHER "BEANO" FOLK ANYWAY?..
M

...MEET "BABY-FACE" MINNIE!
M

"FISH-FACE" MINNIE, YOU MEAN!
SNARL! YOU SHOULDN'T HAVE SAID THAT!
SKID

" Minnie-Face " in a downhill race!

ONLY ONE THING FOR IT!

. . . I'LL HAVE TO BE MINNIE WHIZZ! I'M OFF!
WHIZZ!

TIME TO BE A DIFFERENT "BEANO" CHARACTER.

I'M NOT LORD SNOOTY—I'M LORD MINNIE!

Showing how to take a bow!

FINE! WHAT AN ARTIST I AM!
THE ONLY GOOD THING ABOUT MINNIE IS THERE'S ONLY ONE OF HER.
M
MAN NEXT DOOR
AARGH! I WAS WRONG—IT'S THE THREE MINNIES!

A Menace—but not Dennis!

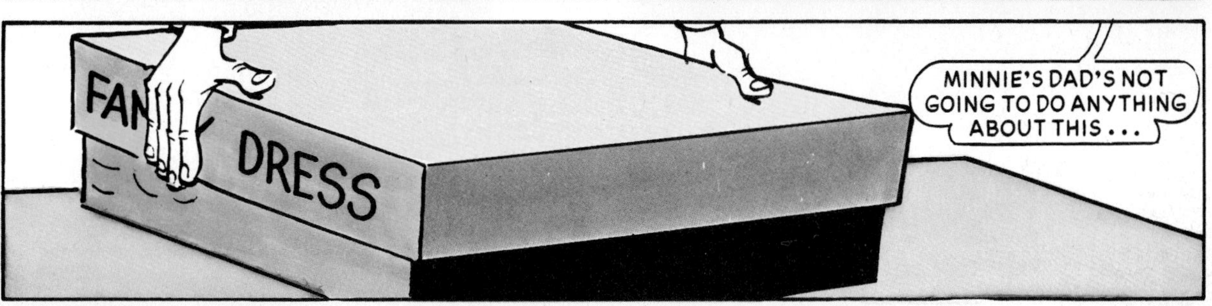

ALL
I'D LOVE TO SWOP HEAD-GEAR WITH SOME FOLK!
MISS WORLD
HOW'S THIS FOR A START?
HELLO, HELLO, HELLO!
DON'T YOU DARE SAY HE LOOKS MORE HANDSOME THAN ME NOW!
NESSIE

CHANGE!

I'M NEARLY AS TALL AS HIM NOW! HEH-HEH!

WHICH ONE'S THE MONA LISA, READERS?

POSH, EH?

But—
GREAT FUN, THIS!
OUCH! THIS IS DEFINITELY THE END OF MY HAT-SWOPPING!

Cast Away!
HOSPITAL
YOU'VE TWISTED YOUR WRIST. KEEP THIS CAST ON FOR A WEEK.
A WEEK? A WEEK? THAT'LL RUIN MY MINXING!
YOU'LL KEEP IT ON FOR A WEEK, MINNIE!
NO-ONE'S LOOKING! I'LL DIVE IN AND DISSOLVE MY PLASTER!
DUCK POND

High and dry!

HEY!

HUH!
YOUR DAD WARNED ME YOU MIGHT TRY THIS!
Parky

Then—
THAT'S FOR ME!
BOXING BOOTH
£5 TO ANYONE LASTING FIVE ROUNDS WITH SLUGGER SMITH

READY TO FIGHT, SLUGGER?
HAW! HAW! WHO LET THAT LITTLE GIRL IN HERE?
SNARL! LITTLE GIRL, IS IT?
SWIPE!
ULP! K- KEEP HER BACK!
REF
TAKE MY PLASTER OFF SO I CAN FIGHT!
REF
YOUR DAD TOLD US TO WATCH OUT FOR YOU!

Sweeping the floor—what a bore!

SIGH! I CAN'T EVEN PLAY FOOTBALL WITH THIS PLASTER ON!
P
BEANOTOWN ALL-STARS

GASP! IT'S ALAN DIGBY, MY FAVOURITE FOOTBALLER!

GROAN! I DON'T HAVE AN AUTOGRAPH BOOK WITH ME!

GOOD OLD ALAN'S SIGNING MY PLASTER!

Here's a shock for the Doc!

...AND THIS IS THE END OF TODAY'S MINXING NEWS...
CLICK!
OFF
BUT YOU CAN KEEP UP TO DATE WITH OUR DEAR DAUGHTER EVERY WEEK IN "THE BEANO" COMIC, READERS!

SMUDGE
TOWN
DUMP
OLD ENGLISH
SHEEPDOG
THAT'S OUR NEIGHBOUR'S
DOG, DINGLE!
THE TIMES

Mud spray—hooray!

EEK!
HELP!
SPLAT!
JAM
WELL, AT LEAST I GOT NICE AND MESSY! FETCH, DINGLE!
WHERE'S THE STICK? AH!
FATTY FORBES
HEY!
SNATCH!
HEH! HEH! FATTY NEEDED TO GO ON A DIET, ANYWAY!

LIQUORICE—MY FAVOURITE!

WHAT A CLEVER DOGGIE!
I LIKE YOU, TOO.

HEY! WHAT'S GOING ON?

LICK! LICK!

TRAITOR! YOU'VE LICKED ME CLEAN AGAIN!

GNASHER SNAPS

THESE HUNGARIAN PULIS ARE VERY RARE, BUT I'M THE ONLY ABYSSINIAN TRIPE-HOUND IN THE WORLD!

BIFFO the BEAR

I'VE GOT A SURPRISE FOR BUSTER!
BUSTER

HAVE A BALLOON, BUSTER!
EH? WHAT FOR?

TWIRL
COME TO MY BIRTHDAY PARTY AT 4 O'CLOCK —Biffo
CHUCKLE! IT'S A SPECIAL INVITATION TO MY PARTY!
AHA!

But—
ERK!
GUST OF WIND

An invite in flight!

THE BASH STREET KIDS

THE BLUE WHALE WITH A RECORDED LENGTH OF 108 FEET AND A WEIGHT OF 131 TONS.
CUTHBERT CRINGEWORTHY, TEACHER'S PET
WHAT IS THE WORLD'S LARGEST MAMMAL?

CUTHBERT'S SO CLEVER, HE EVEN KNOWS THE ANSWER BEFORE I ASK THE QUESTION!
PAT!
SWOT
SWOT
SWOT
SWOT

Cuthbert a bad lot? Surely not!

TRRINNNG!
THE INTERVAL BELL—GOODY!
OUT WITH OUR SNACKS.

SNATCH
SNATCH
SNATCH
ZOOM!

WOW! HE'S BEING AS GREEDY AS FATTY NEXT!
BLOIK!

AND AS SPOTTY AS SPOTTY!

WHAT'S THE MATTER WITH YOU, DEAR BOY?

Examination sensation!

HE'S PICKED UP GERMS FROM THE OTHER CHILDREN—I'M AFRAID HE'S CAUGHT "BASHITIS"!
THERE'S ONLY ONE CURE!
AAAAA . . .
TICKLE
NOW I LOOK LIKE SIDNEY!
...CHOO!
TEACHER GERM

RUN, FELLOWS!

ABANDON CUTHBERT!

FOOTBALL DAFT
is BALL BOY
THIRSTY
YOU'RE SUPPOSED TO SUCK THE HALF-TIME ORANGES, NOT KICK THEM!
DRY

The apple, of course, is for Plum's horse.

. . . YOU'VE TO HOLD IT IN UM PALM OF UM HAND, SO UM HORSE WON'T BITE YOUR FINGERS.
OH!
YUM! IT TASTES GOOD, ACTUALLY.
THAT WAS MY SNACK!
BITE
TREACLE
YEEOW!
ZOOM!
KICK
DROP
SHRIEK!
PRANG
WHAT'S CHIEFY BEEN UP TO?
SHOWING ME HOW NOT TO GET HURT BY HORSES! HEH! HEH!
YOWL!
ACHE

More fun with Speedster Number One!

THUD!
THUD!
THUD!
THUD!
THUD!
OOYAH! OOYAH! OOYAH! OOYAH!
ERK!
PHEW!
ER—MAYBE I SHOULDN'T HAVE TRIED TO TELL HIM HE WAS NEXT ON THE EXERCISE BIKE WHILE HE WAS USING THE SPEEDBALL! GULP!
FLAP!
FLAP!
DOH!
UGH!
Shortly—
RIGHT—START PEDALLING, BILLY. THE SPEEDOMETER WILL TELL YOU HOW FAST YOU WOULD BE GOING IF IT WAS A REAL BIKE.
GASP!

Never seen the like on an exercise bike!

Loose lace—sore face!

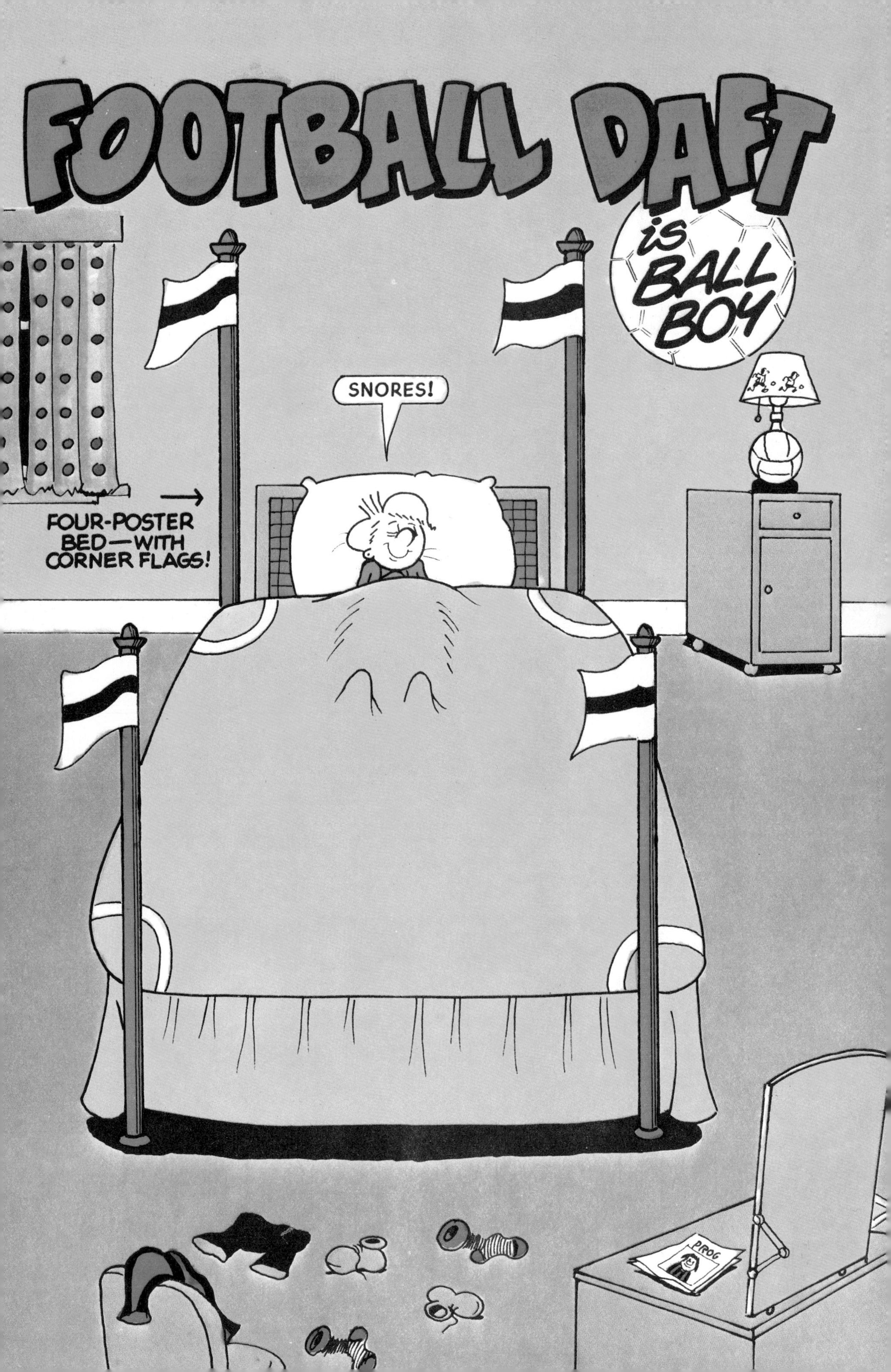
FOOTBALL DAFT
is BALL BOY
SNORES!
FOUR-POSTER BED—WITH CORNER FLAGS!

Bone moan!

PUP PARADE
PEEPS
TUBBY
PUG
BLOTTY
I've buried my bone and I can't find it!
Didn't you mark the ground?
VERY DAFT PUP
SNIFFY
ER-nearly, but I missed!
BONES
WIGGY
MANFRID
'ENRY

I know how to find my bone!
I've borrowed my master's metal detector!
Bones aren't made of metal!
ZOOM!
There must be bones under here!
BLEEP!
ULP!
Who bleeped?

Big dig!

I'll try again!
BLEEP!
Arf! A metal detector just can't find bones!
My bone must be here!

?
?
?
Ah! Here it is!

The metal box I buried my bone in!
BONES

Gasp! He wasn't being stupid, after all!

Now to find the plastic key I locked the box with!
Wrong! He's still as daft as ever!

A GOOD "TYPE"

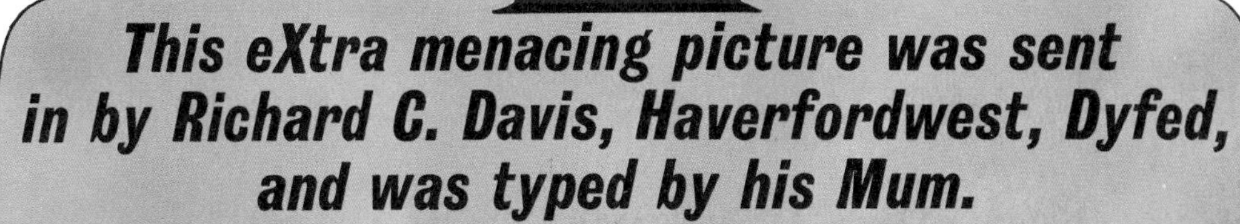
This eXtra menacing picture was sent
in by Richard C. Davis, Haverfordwest, Dyfed,
and was typed by his Mum.

DENNIS The MENACE
and GNASHER
BUS STOP
GNASHER AND I HAVE COME TO ANOTHER TOWN FOR A GNASHING AWAYDAY.
GNESH!
DOING!
OOF!
GNASH! GNASH!
GNASH!
THERE WAS NOTHING LEFT IN OUR TOWN TO GNASH!

GNASH! GNASH! GNASH!
SNIFF! HELLO THERE, YOUNG FELLOW.

COME WITH ME.
CHOMPER

CHOMPER CHOMPS AGAIN
CHAMPION CHOMPER
BEST CHOMPER IN TOWN
CHOMPER CHOMPS FOR THE MAYOR
LOOK AT THESE PRESS CUTTINGS!
I WAS JUST LIKE YOU WHEN I WAS A PUP!
CHOMPER HAS WORN OUT HIS TEETH CHOMPING... MUST LIVE ON GRUEL AND SOUP NOW
BUT LOOK WHAT HAPPENED!
GNEEK!

Later, back home —
BUTCHER
GNASHER GOT SUCH A FRIGHT SEEING CHOMPER THAT HE HASN'T GNASHED SINCE. AH! NOW HE WILL!
← TIGHT LIPPED

FOR YOU, GNASHER!

WH-WHAT?.
BUMP!

AAGH! MY LOVELY MINCER! GET THAT BONE OUT!
PLOP!
SPLUT!
BURP!

Tut-tut! Tough nut!

PEST!
MUST DO SOMETHING TO GET POOR GNASHER GNASHING AGAIN!
DONK!
HAVE A NICE NAP, GNASHER. MAYBE YOU'LL FEEL BETTER AFTERWARDS.
DENNIS'S TOY CUPBOARD
One nap later—
DENNIS'S TOY CUPBOARD
HOPE MY SCHEME WORKS.
BEANO
GNICE GNAP, THAT.

YAWN!
STRETCH
EEK! HORRORS! YIKES!
BEANO

What's wrong? Teeth long!

LORD SNOOTY
TUM-TI-TUM!
OUCH! WHAT'S UP WITH THIS DOOR?
BONK!
THIS IS THE INVISIBLE DOOR GUARDING MACHINE! WHAT'S THE PASSWORD?
GOSH! AUNT MAT MUST HAVE GOT THIS WHEN I WAS OUT!
I'M AFRAID I DON'T KNOW THE PASSWORD.
IN THAT CASE YOU CAN ONLY COME IN IF YOU HAND OVER A WEEK'S SUPPLY OF SWEETS!
HM! NEVER HEARD OF A MACHINE EATING SWEETS! I'LL TRY A LITTLE TEST . . .
WHAT'S TWO PLUS THREE?
ER—ERM— IS IT FOUR?

Gosh! That's a nice line in hats!

GRANDPA

THESE SHOULD DO THE TRICK...

..I CAN EAT MY DINNER NOW.

READING AT THE TABLE! WHERE ARE YOUR MANNERS?

I'LL TAKE THESE!
B—BUT...

PHEW!
THUD!
GET YOUR ELBOWS OFF THE TABLE, SON!
MUNCH!

GLURGH! BUT . . .
DON'T SPEAK WITH YOUR MOUTH FULL— GET YOUR ELBOW OFF!
NNNNNG!
MY ELBOWS ARE OFF NOW!
GRR! GET OFF THE PESKY TABLE!
OK-OK! YOU ASKED FOR IT!

Grub galore—on the floor!

ALL IN A DAY'S WORK
By the BASH ST. SCHOOL JANITOR
7.30 A.M.
TIME TO STOKE THE FURNACE . . .
. . . I'D RATHER BE PLAYING GOLF!
WHACK!
8.30 A.M.
JUST REMEMBERED I HAVEN'T OPENED THE SCHOOL GATES . . .
. . . TEACHER ALREADY KNOWS THAT!
OOYAH!
CLANG!
BASH ST SCHOOL
9.00 A.M.
TIME TO RING THE SCHOOL BELL . . .
. . . AND DISCOVER SOME NAUGHTY CHILD HAS SWAPPED THE CLAPPER FOR A STINK BOMB!
CRACK!
PUTRID PONG
HORRIBLE SMELL
NASTY NIFF
GASP!

9.30 A.M.
THE HEAD WANTS HIS CAR POLISHED TILL HE CAN SEE HIS FACE IN IT . . .
POLISH
. . . HE'S BROKEN HIS SHAVING MIRROR, YOU SEE!
11.00 A.M.
DISCOVER THE KIDS HAVE BEEN USING THE HAIR FROM MY SWEEPING BRUSH FOR THEIR ROLF HARRIS IMPERSONATIONS . . .
. . . BUT SIDNEY VOLUNTEERS TO HELP ME!
SWEEP
2.30 P.M.
TEACHER COMES TO TELL ME THAT A DRAIN'S BLOCKED . . .
KNOCK! KNOCK!
BOILER ROOM
. . I'M WELL AWARE OF THE FACT!
BURBLE!
BOILER ROOM
2.45 P.M.
OLIVE BRINGS ME A CUP OF HER DREADFUL TEA . . .
. . . VERY HANDY FOR UNBLOCKING DRAINS!
OLIVE
GURGLE AWAY
4.00 P.M.
SCHOOL'S OVER FOR THE DAY . . .
'BYE, JANITOR—SEE YOU TOMORROW!
GROAN! THAT'S WHAT I'M AFRAID OF!

GNASHER SNAPS
GROAN! I'LL NEVER BE AN OLD SEA-DOG LIKE HIM! I'M SEA-SICK JUST LOOKING AT WATER!
LK.62.

Not a single sweet, so what can he eat?

ROGER the DODGER

READER'S VOICE
GASP! YOU MUST BE—EATING A BOOK!
CRUNCH!

HEH! IT'S REALLY A DODGE BOOK CAKE, I HAD MADE AT THE BAKERY!

COME AND HELP ME TO WASH MY CAR, ROGER!

OK, DAD—BUT CATCH THIS, FIRST!
?

Have a look at this strange dodge book!

Mending a shelf, all by himself!

FOOTBALL DAFT
is BALL BOY
THAT'S WHAT YOU GET FOR TRYING TO HEADER A WATER-MELON!
DRIP

SMUDGE
Mum's on her ninth load of washing—
SMUDGE'S MUM
GROAN! I'M OUT OF SOAP FLAKES AGAIN!
DAZZLE SOAP FLAKES GIANT SIZE
OFF YOU GO AND BUY SOME SOAP FLAKES.
SPLUD!
ANY EXCUSE TO DIVE INTO MUD!
Soon, at the shops—
MUST GET RID OF THESE HORRIBLE THINGS.
DAZZLE SOAP FLAKES GIANT SIZE
AHA! I'VE GOT AN IDEA!

Soap slope!

PUT THESE ON, MOUSE PAL!
WHAT'S HE UP TO?
"SLUDGE" PET SNAIL

HERE—A SKI-SLOPE FOR YOU!
DAZZLE SOAP FLAKES GIANT SIZE
FLUP!

GOT TO BE KIND TO ANIMALS, DON'T YOU?
WHEE!

Soon—
NOW TO STIR UP SOME MORE SOAP FLAKES IN THIS PUDDLE.

WH-WHERE AM I?

For goodness sake—just one flake!

THE 3 BEARS
YAWN! TIME TO TAKE IN THE MILK FOR BREAKFAST.
OOYAH!
BONK!
PA.
MA.
TED
CHUCKLE! HI, PA—IT'S PLANT-A-TREE WEEK! I SEEM TO HAVE PLANTED THAT ONE IN THE WRONG PLACE! AHEM!

Angry Pa Bear—trees everywhere!

WAH! HE'S GOING TO WRECK OUR HOME!
PA IN DISGUISE
THUD! THUD!
PLEASE, PLEASE, DON'T CHOP DOWN OUR TREE!
WELL, I WON'T IF YOU DO ME A FAVOUR!
ANYTHING! ANYTHING!
So, that night—
TWIT-TWOO! TWIT-TWOO!
TWIT!
TWOO!
HANK'S STORE
GROAN! CAN'T GET TO SLEEP FOR THAT OWLISH NOISE!
And, the next day—
HANK'S TOO TIRED NOW TO STAY AWAKE AND GUARD HIS STORE!
FIENDISHLY CLEVER PLAN, EH, READERS? CHUCKLE!
FRESHLY RAIDED GRUB
HANK'S STORE
ZZZZZZZZZ!

Just the job!

TOM, DICK
AND SALLY'S

PET-WALKING
SERVICE

Then—
YIPPEE! OUR FIRST CUSTOMERS!

So—
WHAT WELL-BEHAVED LITTLE DOGGIES! CHUCKLE!

But—
YIKES! ER—HOLD ON! SLOW DOWN, WILL YOU?

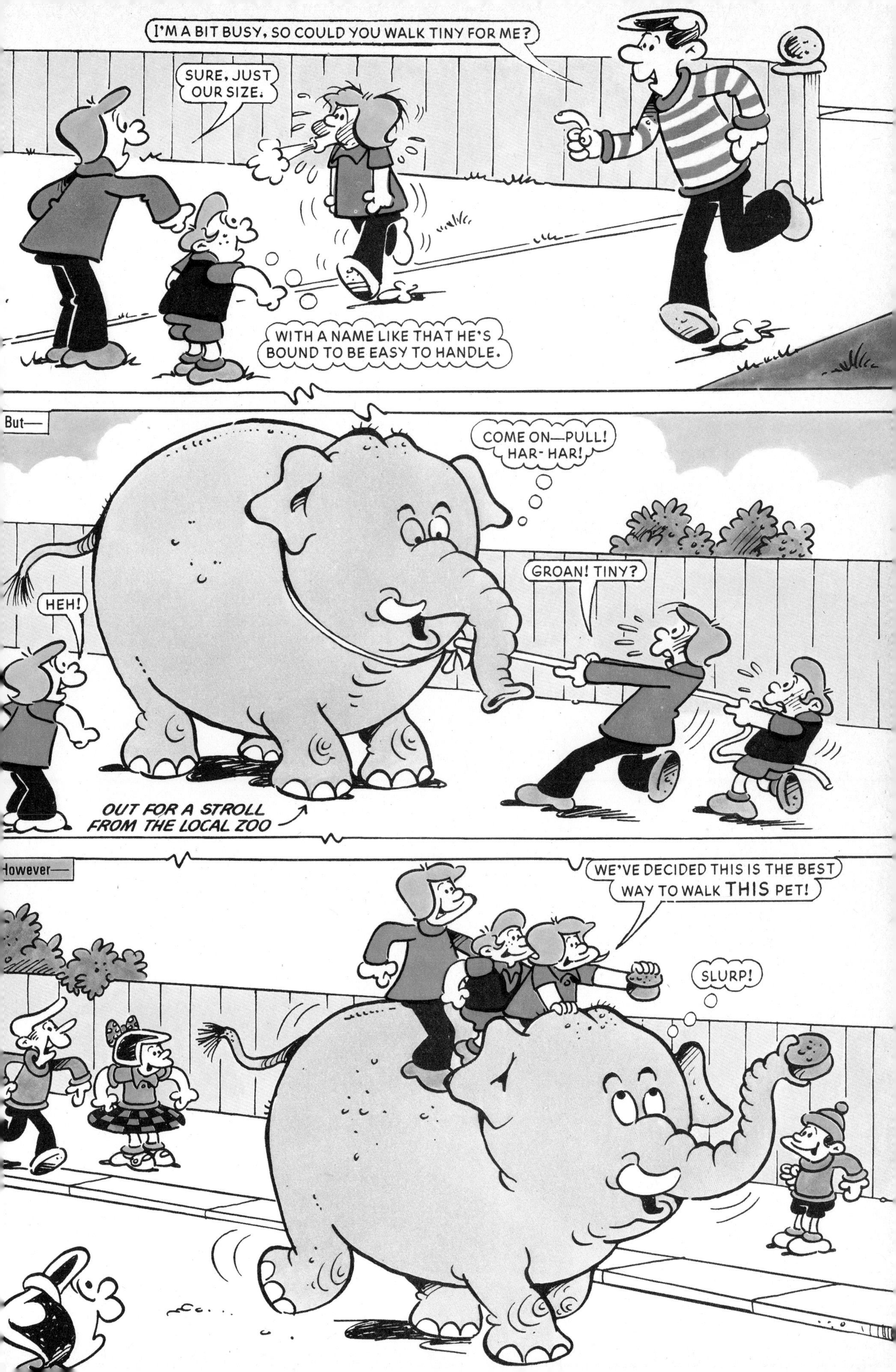
I'M A BIT BUSY, SO COULD YOU WALK TINY FOR ME?
SURE, JUST OUR SIZE.
WITH A NAME LIKE THAT HE'S BOUND TO BE EASY TO HANDLE.
But—
COME ON—PULL! HAR-HAR!
GROAN! TINY?
HEH!
OUT FOR A STROLL FROM THE LOCAL ZOO
However—
WE'VE DECIDED THIS IS THE BEST WAY TO WALK THIS PET!
SLURP!

RASHER'S RECIPE
DENNIS'S PET PIG
HERE'S AN EASY- TO- MAKE DISH FOR WHEN FRIENDS DROP BY FOR SUPPER—" TURNIP SURPRISE "!
TAKE SOME VERY MATURE TURNIP THE RIPER THE BETTER.
WILT
FAINT
PUT SOME OLD TEA LEAVES, RANCID CUSTARD, POTATO PEELINGS AND A TOUCH OF GARLIC POWDER IN A SUITABLE BOWL.
REPLACE THE TOPS AND YOU HAVE A DELICIOUS SNACK YOUR FRIENDS WILL LOVE.
SOFTY WALTER
I OBJECT MOST STRONGLY TO THIS FOUL- SMELLING, DISGUSTING CONCOCTION!

THEN REMOVE THE TOPS.
CHOMP!
NEXT, HOLLOW OUT THE INSIDE, USING A TUSK IF YOU HAVE ONE.
MIX WELL.
THEN FILL THE HOLLOWED-OUT TURNIPS WITH THE MIXTURE.
SPLUTCH!
THAT'S THE " SURPRISE " PART, READERS!
WAH!

I'VE GOT MY LITTLE PAL TO KEEP DENNIS'S BOOTS WARM!
GNASHER SNAPS

Fun afloat with a bandit's boat!

I SHALL HAVE THEM!
DROP
OO!
YUK-SLURP!-YUK!
Soon—
THIS'LL DO FOR DINNER.
H-HEY!
JAB
NAUGHTY BANDIT!
GREAT FISHERMAN I AM!
GLARE

Rise surprise!

ALSO APPEAR EVERY WEEK IN "**THE BEANO**" COMIC

(*OUT ON WEDNESDAYS*) –

AND **LOOK** *AT THE*

2 SUPER BADGES

YOU GET IF YOU JOIN DENNIS'S FABULOUS

FAN CLUB!

SEE

"THE **BEANO**"

FOR FULL DETAILS.

CAN'T I STOP NOW, MR EDITOR?